SHARKS!

PHONICS

Workbook 2

By Quinlan B. Lee

Photo Credits: cover: Fred Bavendam/Minden Pictures/Corbis; title page: Charles Steele/National Geographic; page 2: Michael Patrick O'Neill/Alamy; page 7: Reinhard Dirscherl/age fotostock Spain S.L./Corbis; page 8: Norbert Probst/Alamy; page10: Carlos Villoch/Corbis, Gerald Nowak/Westend61/Corbis; page 11: George Grall/National Geographic; page 13: Greg Amptman/Shutterstock; page 14: Charles Steele/National Geographic; page 16: Carlos Villoch/Corbis

ISBN 978-0-545-74712-7

12 11 10 9 8 7 6 5 4 3 2 1   14 15 16 17 18/0

Printed in China   145

First Printing, September 2014

SCHOLASTIC INC.

Word Scrambles

What *wh* words are these? Unscramble the letters to make *wh* words. Use the word bank to help you.

whine	**whale**	**wham**	**what**

thwa   ____ ____ ____ ____

iwehn   ____ ____ ____ ____

hweal   ____ ____ ____ ____ ____

wmah   ____ ____ ____ ____

Fill in the Blanks

Great **white** sharks are the biggest predators in the world! Do you know other facts about great **whites**? Fill in the blanks with *wh* words to make more great **white** facts.

whiff	whip	whimper	white

A great white shark has a gray back and _____ belly.

Great whites can smell a _____ of blood from three miles away.

Great whites can _____ out of the water to get a seal.

Great whites can hear a little _____ . They have great hearing.

D1092614

Spot the Words

Sharks can **spot** prey in the dark. Sharks can **spot** prey in the deep. How about you? Can you **spot** the *s-blend* words in the word search below?

snout	**stare**	**smell**
skin	**strip**	**sneak**

q h y s m e l l z

s k i n d r i v e

n e e o s t r i p

e e e u k o n g x

a s s t a r e e e

k s h a r k s g o

Word Families

Sharks have a **strong** sense of **smell**. They **smell** with **small slits** in their **snouts**. Can you make more words that belong in the word families of **smell** and **snout**? Use the *s-blends* below to help you.

s	sc	sh	sp
spr	st	sw	

smell   **snout**

_____ell   _____out

_____ell   _____out

_____ell   _____out

_____ell   _____out

                                      _____out

Complete the Sentences

Even though whale sharks have "whale" in their name, they are not whales. They **breathe** through gills, so they are fish. Fill in the correct *r-blend* words below to find out more about whale sharks.

Whale shark spots are like finger _____.

drink   **prints**

Whale sharks eat small shrimp called _____.

krill   **gill**

Whale sharks close their mouths to trap _____.

prey   **try**

Whale sharks do not like to swim in a _____.

truck   **group**

Find the Rhymes

Whale sharks **breathe** through gills and eat **krill**. Gill and **krill** rhyme. In the rows below, two of the *r-blend* words rhyme and one does not. Put an X through the word that does not rhyme.

1. crab   gray   grab

2. trash   crash   trap

3. try   prey   cry

4. group   grow   crow

5. gray   tray   truck

Word Clues

Hammerhead shark heads are **flat** and **blunt**. No other sharks look like them! Hammer out some words by adding an *l-blend* from the box below.

bl	cl	fl	pl	sl

_____ue   the color of many fish

_____oor   the sandy bottom of the sea

_____ice   to cut through

_____ay   to have fun

_____amp   to hold tight

Unscramble and Match

Hammerheads can **blast** through the water when they **slide** their tails from side to side. Draw a line from the scrambled letters to the *l-blend* word that they make. **Blast** as fast as you can!

edeps   blend

ceols   sleek

ldneb   glide

deigl   speed

leske   close

Get the Fish

Hammerheads can find fish even if they **blend** in with the sandy ocean **floor**. Help the hammerhead get to the fish by coloring in the *l-blend* words in the puzzle below.

	blunt	close	sling	prey	whale
shark	what	gray	glide	sleek	whine
chomp	crab	sandy	when	play	white
over	teeth	slide	clue	blue	great
land	can	blast	attack	smell	krill
ride	grab	place	blend	flat	

Rhyme Time

Sand tiger sharks **blend** in with the **sand**. In the rows below draw a circle around the words that rhyme with **blend** and draw a box around the words that rhyme with **sand**.

1. bland   teeth   end   send

2. spend   tiger   find   land

3. sharp   hand   tend   waves

4. grand   kind   end   ray

Hidden Words

Sand tiger sharks can **blend** in with the waves. Words can **blend** into a word search. Find the **nd** words in the box and circle them.

> blend   find   spend
>
> kind   sand   land

s	h	a	r	f	k	s
q	u	b	s	i	n	c
a	h	l	a	n	d	k
s	p	e	n	d	n	d
h	d	n	d	c	a	n
s	j	d	k	i	n	d

Take a Closer Look

A **sand** tiger shark is not as scary as it looks. One word in each of the rows below is not a word that ends with **nd**. Mark it with an X.

1. ring   find   sand   spend

2. kind   plane   end   land

3. blend   sing   tend   hand

4. fine   send   and   mind

Match the Rhymes

You can find sharks in any ocean in the world. Can you find words that rhyme? Draw a line between the words that rhyme below.

tend   sand

smell   grab

land   slide

crab   spend

glide   swell

Unscramble the Sentences

Unscramble the sentences below to find out facts about different sharks.

biggest the fish. sharks Whale are

_____

_____

have sharks flat Hammerhead heads.

_____

_____

float. tiger can Sand sharks

_____

_____

Answer Key

p. 2

  what, whine, whale, wham

p. 3

  white, whiff, whip, whimper

p. 4

```
q  h  y (s  m  e  l  l) z
(s  k  i  n) d  r  i  v  e
 n  e  e  o (s  t  r  i  p)
 e  e  e  u  k  o  n  g  x
 a  s (s  t  a  r  e) e  e
 k  s  h  a  r  k  s  g  o
```

p. 5
smell	**snout**
sell	scout
shell	shout
spell	spout
swell	sprout
	stout

p. 6

  prints, krill, prey, group

p. 7

 ① crab   ~~gray~~   grab

 ② trash   crash   ~~trap~~

 ③ try   ~~prey~~   cry

 ④ ~~group~~   grow   crow

 ⑤ gray   tray   ~~truck~~

p. 8

  blue, floor, slice, play, clamp

p. 9

edeps ———— blend
ceols ———— sleek
ldneb ———— glide
deigl ———— speed
leske ———— close

p. 10

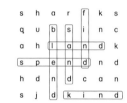

	blunt	close	sling	prey	whale
shark	what	gray	glide	sleek	whine
chomp	crab	sandy	when	play	white
over	teeth	slide	clue	blue	great
land	con	blast	attack	smell	krill
ride	grab	place	blend	flat	

p. 11

 ① [bland] teeth (end) (send)

 ② (spend) tiger find [land]

 ③ sharp [hand] (tend) waves

 ④ [grand] kind (end) ray

p. 12

```
s  h  a  r [f] k  s
q  u [b][s] i  n  c
a  h [l  a  n  d] k
(s  p  e  n  d) n  d
h  d  n [d] c  a  n
s  j [d  k  i  n  d]
```

p. 13

 ① ~~ring~~ find sand spend

 ② kind ~~plane~~ end land

 ③ blend ~~sing~~ tend hand

 ④ ~~fire~~ send and mind

p. 14

tend ———— sand
smell ———— grab
land ———— slide
crab ———— spend
glide ———— swell

p. 15

  Whale sharks are the biggest fish.
  Hammerhead sharks have flat heads.
  Sand tiger sharks can float.

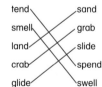

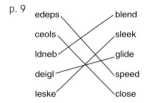